Maths Challenge

Graded problems for 9–12 year-olds

Anne Joshua

STANLEY
THORNES

Copyright © Longman Cheshire 1991

First published in 1991 by
Longman Cheshire Pty Limited, Australia

Reprinted in 1994 by Simon & Schuster Education

This edition published exclusively for W H Smith 1996 by
Stanley Thornes (Publishers) Ltd
Ellenborough House
Wellington Street
Cheltenham GL50 1YW

97 98 99 00 / 10 9 8 7 6

Designed by Norma van Rees
Illustrations by Boris Silvestri
Set in Plantin Light 12½/14½pt.
Printed in Great Britain by The Baskerville Press, Salisbury, Wiltshire

A catalogue record of this book is available from the British
Library

ISBN 0–7487–2104–5

Contents

Introduction

This series of four books will help to stimulate and challenge your child to think and develop mathematically, enabling them to relate mathematics to everyday life and to think logically and more strategically.

The activities, which all support National Curriculum mathematics and are excellent examples of good practice in mathematics, are graded to allow you to observe and participate in your child's development. The activities are lively and will really get your child thinking.

Here are some practical suggestions on how you can help:

- Ensure your child understands the question.

- Where do I start? Beginning is often a block for children; encourage them, pretend to be a detective and see what clues you have already.

- Encourage your child to have the confidence to have a go.

- In some of the activities there could be several solutions; let your child know that there may be many different ways to solve the question.

- Can you find a pattern? Asking your child if he/she can see any common features is a major step in mathematical thinking. Once children begin to see and explore patterns, they gain confidence and are often able to use the information gathered again in a new situation.

- Let's get organised!

  Encourage your child to put thoughts on paper, firstly so that he/she can make sense of them and, then, so that others are able to understand the notes he/she makes. This is an important aspect of mathematics. This may need some help from you. Show your child how you would set the information out: it will give clues and demonstrate the need to be systematic. Getting organised is one aspect of mathematics which will take time. . . it requires patience and understanding.

- Can you find a rule? Many of the activities in the books will encourage your child to find a rule and check whether the rule works in all cases. Encourage your child to reflect on the problem he/she has solved and to discuss what he/she has learnt from it.

- Keep a record of your child's work and look back on the progress he/she has made.

What's the value?

Each figure in these equations stands for one of the digits 1 to 9.
Which is which?

    This is a difficult problem — can you solve it?

1   ▨ + ◫ = ⊠

2   ◫ × ⊞ = ▦

3   ◧ + ◫ = ◫

4   ◧ × ◫ = ◧

5   ◫ + ◧ = ◫ × ◧

6   ⊠ ÷ ⊞ = ⊞

7   ☐ ÷ ◧ = ◧

8   ☐ + ◫ = ▣

9   ⊠ + ◧ = ⊠

10   ⧅ − ☐ = ▣

11   ▣ + ◫ = ◹

Rolling boxes

Boxes of various shapes have to be moved to a different position by turning them end over end, not by pushing or sliding them.

Can you place the symbols in the positions they will have each time a box is turned? Experiment by cutting out a box shape for each exercise, drawing the symbols on it and turning the shape as the box would roll.

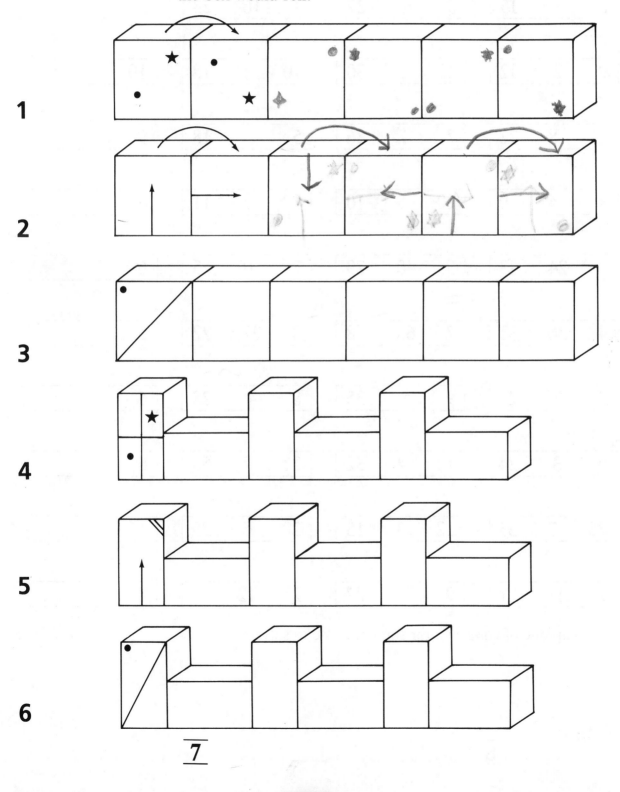

1

2

3

4

5

6

Find my rule

In each set of boxes, every box follows the same rule. Find the rule, write it down, and then work out which numbers are missing.

1 | 2 8 15 | 5 20 27 | 4 16 23 | 3 |

2 | 9 2 12 | 12 5 30 | 10 3 18 | 10 |

3 | 11 8 72 | 7 4 36 | 5 2 18 | 9 |

4 | 8 4 9 | 10 5 10 | 12 6 11 | 6 |

5 | 3 24 13 | 5 40 29 | 2 16 5 | 6 |

6 | 4 36 31 | 7 63 58 | 3 27 22 | 5 |

7 | 7 3 21 | 9 5 35 | 8 4 28 | 6 |

8 | 9 3 24 | 12 4 32 | 21 7 56 | 6 |

9 | 28 7 35 | 12 3 15 | 20 5 25 | 16 |

10 | 7 42 21 | 9 54 27 | 2 12 | 8 |

Make up one of your own for someone else to solve.

Digits and numbers

Can you work out and write down:

1   The largest 4-digit number that has 5 as one of its digits.

2   The smallest 4-digit number that has 5 as one of its digits.

3   The smallest 4-digit number.

4   The largest 5-digit number.

5   The smallest 4-digit number in which no digit is repeated.

6   The largest 4-digit number in which no digit is repeated.

7   The largest 4-digit number that contains the digits 2 and 7 and in which no digit is repeated.

8   The largest 3-digit number that uses the three smallest prime numbers.

9   The smallest 3-digit number that uses the three smallest prime numbers.

10   The smallest 4-digit number that has one 0 digit.

11   The largest 4-digit number that has one 0 digit.

12   The smallest 5-digit number.

13   The smallest 5-digit number in which the digit 0 is not used.

14   The largest 5-digit number in which the digits 9, 7 and 6 are not used.

15   The largest 4-digit number that has one 0 digit and in which no digit is repeated.

Picture graphs

These graphs give us information by means of pictures.

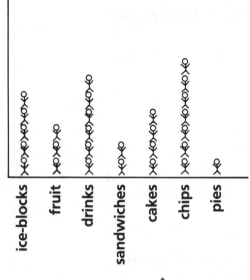

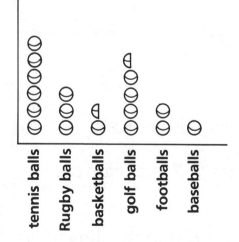

1 The picture graph opposite shows the number of children who bought various items at the snackbar.

Each ⚲ represents 3 children, and each child bought only one item.

(a) How many children bought a drink?

(b) How many children bought an ice-block?

(c) How many children bought a piece of cake?

(d) Which item was the most popular? How many children bought it?

(e) Which item was the least popular? How many children bought it?

(f) Altogether, how many children were served?

(g) If 15 sandwiches were prepared, how many were left over?

2 This picture graph shows the number of balls sold in one week by a sports shop. Each ⊖ represents 4 balls.

(a) How many of each of these balls were sold?
   (i) tennis balls
   (ii) footballs
   (iii) basketballs
   (iv) golf balls

(b) How many balls were sold altogether?

3 What else could you find out from these graphs? Make up some questions of your own and answer them.

Problem solving: Working systematically 1

1 Can you colour these flags in six different ways, using the colours red, blue and yellow, if each colour can be used only once on each flag?

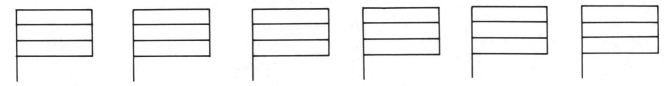

2 Using flags with three stripes, as in question 1, how many different combinations can you make with the colours red, blue and yellow if each colour can be used once, twice or three times in each flag?

Two possible combinations are shown at left.

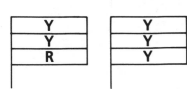

3 On the diagrams below, show that there are ten different paths that Edward can take from his home to his school, five blocks away. One possible route is drawn for you.

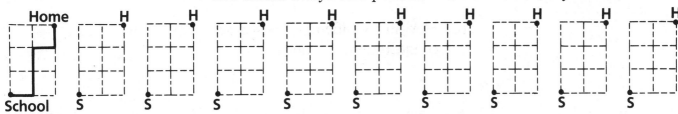

4 Gloria decides to make a circular bracelet for herself by threading three red and three white beads on a string. How many different patterns of red and white can she make?

Here is one possibility:

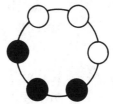

The bracelet can be turned around and these two patterns can be considered to be the same as the first. What do you think?

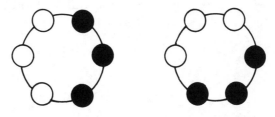

How many?

Remember to work systematically in answering these questions. For example, to find the total number of triangles in the figure at left, you could:

first count all the single triangles	:	5
next look for double triangles (in this case, none)	:	0
then count the large triangles (shown below)	:	5
		10

1 How many triangles are there in this star?
   Don't forget to count the single little triangles, the middle-sized triangles and the large triangles.

2 **(a)** How many different line segments can be drawn to connect these four dots?

   (b) How many different line segments can be drawn to connect these five dots?

3 How many parallelograms can you find in the figure at left?

   Don't forget to count first the small parallelograms and then those that are double (containing two), treble (containing three), quadruple (containing four) and large (containing six).

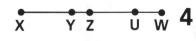

4 XY and XZ are two segments of this line. How many different line segments can you name?

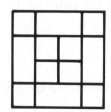

5 How many squares can you find in this figure?

Multiplication table squares

You may have been asked to complete multiplication table squares like square number 1.

Now, the challenge in numbers 2 to 8 is to find some of the numbers that have to be multiplied as well as to complete the squares. The missing numbers that have to be multiplied are all less than 12.

1

×	3	5	4	7
2	6	10	8	
8	24			
3				
9				

2

×	4	6	↗	
5			10	
↗		18		21
↗	32			
			12	

You can start square 2 by filling in any of the spaces marked with an arrow.

3

×		3		
	4		18	
		24		
7	14			35
			36	

4

×		4		
	14	22		
		12	15	
9	63			
			44	

5

×		8		
			20	40
		40		
3			15	
	27			90

6

×			7	
3				24
		16	56	
	54	12		
	18			

7

×		4		
		4		8
	30			48
	45	54		
		16		

8

×		2		
	25			
8				64
			6	
		100		

How does it start?

What numbers belong in the START circles of these flow charts? Here is an example:

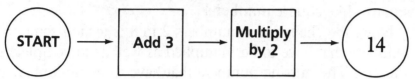

Begin with the final number and work backwards (that is, use the inverse of each operation).

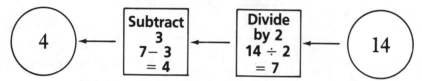

You could now check this solution like this:

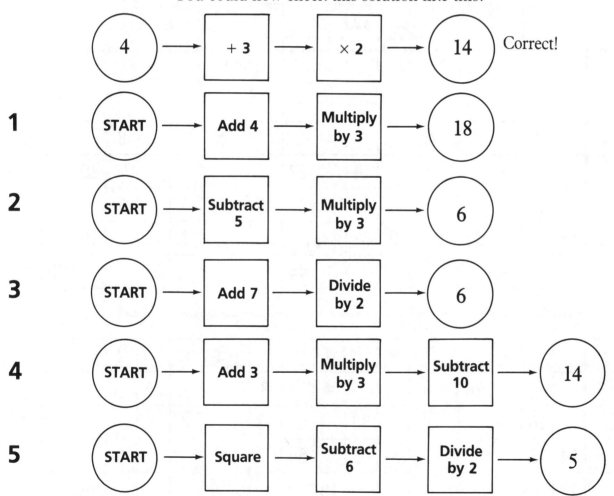

6 Try changing some of the end numbers. Can a number always be found for the start?

Investigating magic squares

A square is said to be magic when the numbers in all horizontal, vertical and diagonal lines have the same sum.

8	1	6
3	5	7
4	9	2

This is an example of a magic square. It has a magic sum of 15, which is the sum of the numbers in all horizontal, vertical and diagonal lines.

10	3	8
5	7	9
6	11	4

1 Add 2 to each number in the example square above, giving this new square on the left. Is it still magic?

2 Now add 10 to each number in the example square above. Is it still magic?

3 Investigate what happens to the example square when you:
(a) subtract 1 from each number;
(b) multiply each number by 2;
(c) multiply each number by 3, 5 or 10;
(d) divide each number by 2;
(e) add ½ to (or subtract ½ from) each number.
Is the square still magic in each case? Explain.

1	14	7	12
15	4	9	6
10	5	16	3
8	11	2	13

4 Investigate what happens to this 4 × 4 magic square when to each number you:
(a) add 1, 2, 3, 10 or any number;
(b) subtract 1, ½;
(c) multiply by 2, 3, 10 or any number;
(d) divide by 2.

Is the square still magic in every case?
Try to explain your answer.

Counting cubes

Count the number of cubes that will be needed to build each of the towers below. To do this, first count the number of cubes in each layer, as set out in group 1. What patterns can you see?

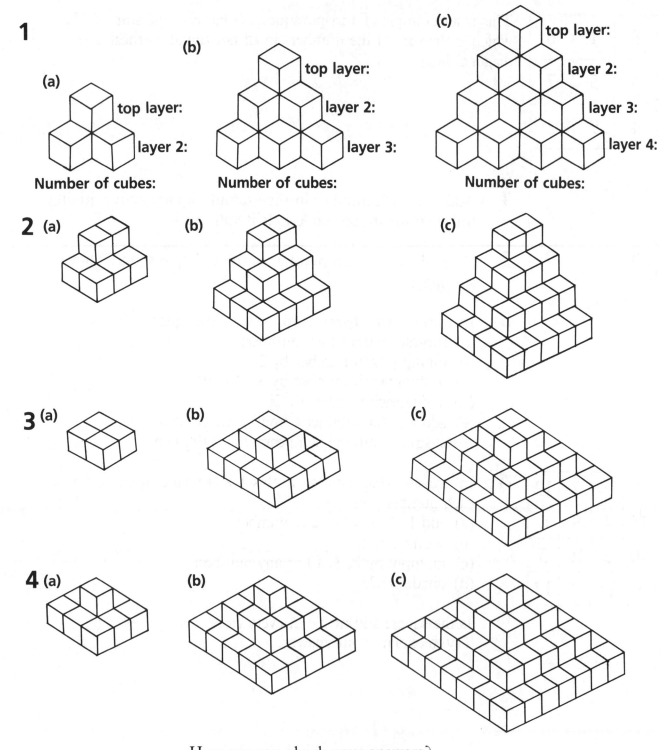

1

(a) top layer:
layer 2:
Number of cubes:

(b) top layer:
layer 2:
layer 3:
Number of cubes:

(c) top layer:
layer 2:
layer 3:
layer 4:
Number of cubes:

2 (a)   **(b)**   **(c)**

3 (a)   **(b)**   **(c)**

4 (a)   **(b)**   **(c)**

How can you check your answers?

Puzzles with shapes

1 Using 1 cm squared paper, copy and cut out these two identical triangles:

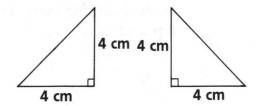

By matching sides of the cut pieces, it is possible to make a parallelogram, as shown.

What other shapes can you make with the two triangles?

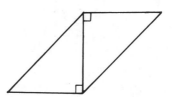

2 Again using 1 cm squared paper, copy and cut out five rectangles measuring 6 cm × 4 cm and seven rectangles measuring 7 cm × 4 cm.

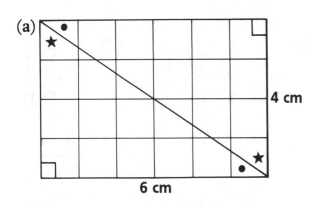

(a)

6 cm

4 cm

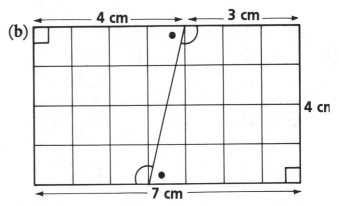

(b)

4 cm   3 cm

4 cm

7 cm

Cut all the 6 cm × 4 cm rectangles along the diagonals, and by matching edges from the cut pieces try to make five different shapes.

Cut all the 7 cm × 4 cm rectangles along an oblique line, as shown above, and by matching edges from the cut pieces try to make seven different shapes.

Glue all the different shapes in your book.

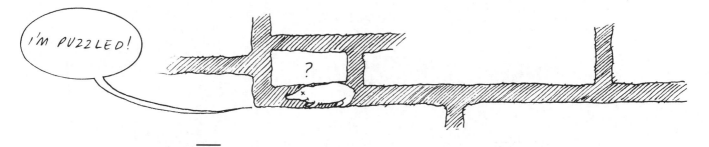

I'M PUZZLED!

?

Letter values

In the following exercises, the letters represent digits. No digit is repeated in any one exercise. Find the value of each letter.

1
```
  B 1
    B ×
─────
2 B B
```

2
```
  C 1
    C ×
─────
3 C C
```

3
```
4 A
  A ×
─────
2 7 A
```

4
```
M N
  3 ×
─────
6 9
```

5
```
U V W
    6 ×
───────
1 4 8 2
```

6
```
P
Q +
───
R R
```

7
```
D
E
F +
───
D F
```

8
```
J K
  K +
───
K J
```

9
```
L G
  L +
─────
G H H
```

10
```
C D
C D
C D
C D +
─────
E C
```

11
```
Y Y
W W
X X +
─────
W X Y
```

12
```
P Q
P Q
Q P +
─────
S S S
```

13
```
W T W
  V W −
─────
  W T
```

14
```
L M N
L M N
L M N +
───────
N N N
```

15
```
A A B
B B A +
───────
B B B D
```

Problem solving: Working systematically 2

Working systematically through these problems will help you to account for all possibilities and avoid repetitions.

1   Four good friends — Robert, Yasu, Simon and Hassan — buy presents for each other for their birthdays.
  (a)   How many presents must each person buy?
  (b)   How many presents are bought altgether?

2   A family of five buy presents for each other. How many presents are bought altogether?

3   How many different three-letter code words can you make using the letters A, B and C:
  (a)   if repetition of the letters *is not* permitted;
  (b)   if repetition of the letters *is* permitted.

4   Three friends — Amanda (A), Michelle (M) and Sarah (S) are in a race at a carnival. List the number of different ways in which they could come first, second and third. (In your working, use their initials, as shown above.)

5   In how many ways can you put five fish in two bowls so that each bowl has at least one fish in it?

6   Winston goes away for the weekend and takes with him a blue and a yellow shirt, a navy and a white pair of shorts, and a black and a red jumper.
   How many different three-piece outfits can he make? Use a table like this to list the possibilities.

Shirts	Shorts	Jumpers

7   I have only a 2 g, a 5 g and a 10 g mass. How many different exact weights can I measure with these?

8   I have four 10p stamps and three 20p stamps. If I use one or more of these stamps, list the different amounts of postage I can make.

Problem solving: Working backwards

In each of these questions, I am thinking of a number. Examine the clues given, and then work backwards to find my numbers.

1 If you add 3 to the number and multiply the result by 2, you get 18.

2 If you double the number and then double the result, you get 20.

3 If you halve the number and then add 4, you get 10.

4 If you subtract 7 from the number and double the result, you get 12.

5 If you halve the number and then add 9, you get 14.

6 If you halve the number and double the result, you get 8.

7 If you double the number and halve the result, you get 6.

8 If you double the number and then subtract 4, you get 6.

9 If you add 6 to the number and then halve the result, you get 7.

10 If you subtract 3 from the number and multiply the result by 5, you get 30.

11 If you multiply the number by 5 and then subtract 3, you get 17.

12 If you halve the number and then halve the result, you get 4.

13 If you multiply the number by itself (square it), you get 16.

14 If you square the number and then add 1, you get 10.

15 If you subtract 4 and square the result, you get 16.

16 If you subtract 7, then square the result you get 4.

17 If you multiply the number by 9 and then add 3, you get 30.

18 If you square the number and then add 7, you get 23.

19 If you square the number, then add 2 and halve the result, you get 3.

20 Make up some of these of your own.

Problem solving: Using tables 1

Draw up tables and use guess-and-check to solve these problems.

1 Esi and Marc collect marbles. Esi has 3 more marbles than Marc. Together they have 21.
How many marbles does each have?

Esi	Marc	Total marbles

2 Mrs Kind bought a total of 14 ice-creams and ice-lollies for her children and their friends. Ice-creams cost £1 each, while ice-lollies cost 50p each. If Mrs Kind spent £10 altogether, how many of each did she buy?

Ice-creams (£1)	Ice-lollies (50p)	Total spent

3 John has some 5p and 10p coins in his pocket.
Find out how many of each coin John has if:
(a) he has 40p altogether and a total of 6 coins;
(b) he has 80p altogether and a total of 11 coins;
(c) he has 45p altogether and a total of 6 coins;
(d) he has 70p altogether and a total of 8 coins;
(e) he has 50p altogether and a total of 8 coins.

5p coins	10p coins	Total coins	Total amount

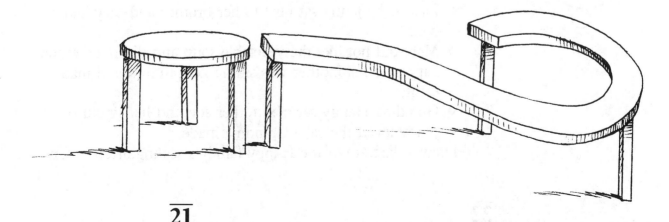

Problem solving: With extra information

Sometimes in solving problems you may find you have more information than you need. In these exercises, you will have to work out which is the relevant data.

1   Ade weighed 44 kg; he weighed 12 kg more than Steve. Yoko weighed 9 kg more than Steve. How much did Steve weigh?

2   Four girls competed in the high jump at the school carnival. Layla, who is 13 years old, jumped 6 cm higher than Lisa. Lisa jumped 3 cm lower than Kate, but 2 cm higher than Zara. Zara and Lisa are cousins.

   If Kate jumped 95 cm, how high did the other three girls jump?

3   The same four girls also competed in the long jump.

   Layla jumped 5 cm further than Lisa and 8 cm further than Kate. Zara jumped 10 cm further than Lisa and 4 cm further than her best friend, Rhonda.

   If Kate jumped 252 cm, how far did the other girls jump?

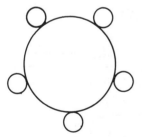

4   The Happy family — Mr Happy, Mrs Happy, Marc, Jenny and Grandma Happy — were sitting at their round kitchen table, having dinner.
  ● Mrs Happy did not sit next to her husband.
  ● Jenny sat next to her father.
  ● Last night Jenny sat next to her brother and they had a fight.
  ● Marc did not like the vegetable soup and did not feel too happy, as his mother was sitting next to him and made him eat it.
  ● Grandma Happy sat next to her son and her grandson.
  ● Jenny loved the cake Grandma made.
Draw a diagram of the Happy family's seating arrangement.

Perimeter and area investigation

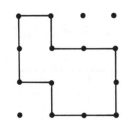

The *perimeter* of a figure is the distance around it.

The *area* of a figure is the amount of surface enclosed by it.

This figure has a perimeter of 12 units and an area of 6 square units.

1 In the table below, the perimeters and the areas of figures are given. Draw each of these figures on dot paper or construct them on a geoboard.

    The sides of all figures must be horizontal or vertical.

	Perimeter (units)	Area (square units)
(a)	4	1
(b)	6	2
(c)	8	4
(d)	10	4
(e)	10	5
(f)	12	5*
(g)	10	6
(h)	12	8
(i)	12	9
(j)	16	16

★ There are many possible solutions to (f). How many can you find?

2 Now try to draw a figure with a perimeter of 13 units and an area of 5 square units. Explain.

Growing squares and triangles

1 **(a)** Here is a square that is growing in size.

Work out the perimeter and the area of each size, and record your answers in your own way.

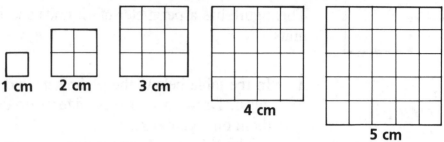

1 cm   2 cm   3 cm   4 cm   5 cm

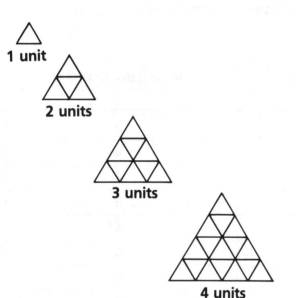

1 unit

2 units

3 units

4 units

5 units

(b) Can you predict the perimeter and the area of squares whose sides are (a) 6 cm and (b) 10 cm?

2 An *equilateral* triangle is a triangle whose three sides are the same length.

(a) Here is an equilateral triangle that is growing in size.

Work out the perimeter and the area of each size, and record your answers. A table like the one below may be helpful.

 1 triangular grid

 Since 4 grids fit into this larger triangle, its area is 4 triangular grids.

Side (units)	Perimeter (units)	Area (triangular grids)
1	3	1
2	6	4
3		
4		
5		

(b) Can you predict the perimeters and the areas (measured in triangular grids) of equilateral triangles whose sides measure (a) 6 units and (b) 10 units?

24

Perimeter puzzles

Use squared paper to draw the figures in these exercises.

1 **(a)** Find the perimeter of this figure, which is made up of four squares each with sides of 1 cm.
(b) With the four squares used in (a), can you draw other figures that have the same perimeter as the original one?

2 Arrange four squares, each with sides of 1 cm, to make a perimeter of:
(a) 14 cm
(b) 12 cm
(c) 10 cm
(d) 8 cm
Draw as many different figures as you can with each measurement.

3 The perimeter of a square field is 36 m. What is the length of each side?

4 The perimeter of a rectangular field is 60 m. If the length is twice the width, what is the length of the field?

5 The length of a rectangular field is three times the width and the perimeter of the field is 48 m. Find the length and the width.

6 Four square tables are pushed next to each other to form one large table. If the perimeter of the new large table is 20 m, what is the perimeter of one square table?

Palindromic numbers

MY NAME IS ANNA, FORWARDS AND BACKWARDS.

The numbers 121, 797 and 3443 are all examples of palindromic numbers, since they read the same both forwards and backwards.

It is very interesting that, starting with any two-digit number, you can make (generate) a palindromic number in the following way:

Start with a two-digit number : 13

Reverse the digits : 31

These numbers required *one stage* to become palindromic.

Add, to make a palindromic number : 44

Now start with this number : 47

Reverse the digits : 74

Add, to make a palindromic number : 121

However:

If you start with this number : 39

Reverse the digits : 93   This number is not yet palindromic.

and add : 132

So you must repeat the process.

Reverse the digits : 231   Number 39 took *two stages* to become palindromic.

Add again : 363

1 Show that to become palindromic:
   (a) 59 requires three stages;
   (b) 78 requires four stages;
   (c) 79 requires six stages.

2 Investigate how many stages numbers less than 100 take to become palindromic. Are there any patterns?

3 'Noon' and 'madam' are examples of palindromic words. Write down as many palindromic words as you can find.

Shopping at a barter market

Sometimes people swap goods for other goods, instead of using money. This kind of trading is called a barter system.

At one particular barter market:

10 potatoes = 5 apples = 2 tomatoes = 1 lettuce

which means that one lettuce can be traded for any of the first three items.

Therefore, 2 lettuces are worth 4 tomatoes or 10 apples or 20 potatoes.

1   If I have 3 lettuces, how many of each of the following can I trade for them?
   (a) tomatoes
   (b) apples
   (c) potatoes

2   How many lettuces will I need if I want to obtain these goods?
   (a) 10 tomatoes
   (b) 20 apples
   (c) 60 potatoes

3   Calculate how many apples I will need if I want to obtain:
   (a) 4 tomatoes
   (b) 20 tomatoes
   (c) 50 potatoes
   (d) 6 lettuces

4   If I have 25 apples, how many of each of the following can I trade for them?
   (a) lettuces
   (b) tomatoes
   (c) potatoes

5   If I have 10 tomatoes and 10 apples, how many lettuces can I trade for them?

6   If I want to obtain 16 tomatoes, how many of each of the following will I need to swap for them?
   (a) lettuces
   (b) apples
   (c) potatoes

Tree diagrams

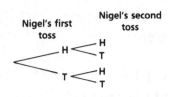

Here is an example of a tree diagram.

If Nigel is tossing a 10p coin, each toss can turn up either heads (H) or tails (T). When Nigel tosses the coin twice, the possible results are HH, HT, TH or TT.

A tree diagram can be very helpful in working out this type of problem. Read along the branches of the first diagram to give all the possibilities described.

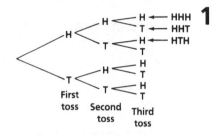

1 If Nigel tossed a coin three times, a tree diagram would look like the one at left.

Continue to write down all the possibilities.

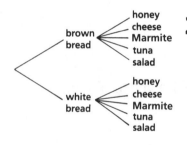

2 Every morning Malcolm makes his own sandwich. He can use brown or white bread and can choose between honey, cheese, Marmite, tuna or salad filling. Using the tree diagram on the left, work out the number of variations Malcolm can use.

3 Edwyn and Barry are planning to go to Brighton Marina. They can travel from home to the town by train, coach or car. From the town they can go to Brighton Marina by walking, catching a bus or taking a taxi.

List the various ways in which they can travel from home to Brighton Marina.

You can either draw a tree diagram *or* represent the information with a drawing.

Number squares

Find the values of the letters A, B, C, D and E in these squares. The sum of each row and column is given, and only the numbers 1, 2, 3, 4 and 5 have been used. Starting with the one letter-value given for each square, you will be able to work out the others.

1

A	A	C	B	10
B	E	B	D	17
E	E	C	D	11
B	D	A	C	12
15	12	9	14	

A   B   C   D   E

2

2	2			10
				17
				11
			2	12
15	12	9	14	

2

D	A	D	B	8
C	C	A	B	12
E	D	C	A	12
A	E	B	C	13
12	12	10	11	

A   B   C   D   E

        4

				8
4	4			12
		4		12
			4	13
12	12	10	11	

3

E	D	C	A	11
E	C	B	A	10
D	A	C	E	11
C	A	B	D	12
12	10	10	12	

A   B   C   D   E

                    3

3				11
3				10
			3	11
				12
12	10	10	12	

4

B	B	D	C	15
D	D	A	C	13
E	A	C	E	9
E	C	B	D	14
15	12	12	12	

A   B   C   D   E

            5

		5		15
5	5			13
				9
			5	14
15	12	12	12	

Strange maths symbols

In these exercises, new signs have been introduced to represent various uses of the symbols ×, +, − and ÷. Each exercise follows a particular rule.

Here is an example:

$3 \boxtimes 2 = 25$ $2 \boxtimes 4 = 36$

$7 \boxtimes 1 = 64$ $1 \boxtimes 3 = ?$

This rule is 'Add the two numbers, then square the result (or multiply the result by itself); so that $\square \boxtimes \triangle = (\square + \triangle)^2$.

Therefore $1 \boxtimes 3 = (1 + 3)^2$

$= 4^2$

$= 16$

Find the rule in each exercise and complete the final number sentence.

1 $3 \odot 4 = 12$
$5 \odot 9 = 19$
$8 \odot 2 = 15$
$7 \odot 3 = ?$
Hint: Try adding.

2 $7 \wedge 2 = 7$
$9 \wedge 3 = 8$
$5 \wedge 1 = 6$
$6 \wedge 4 = 4$
$8 \wedge 2 = ?$
Hint: Try subtracting.

3 $5 \star 1 = 7$
$3 \star 4 = 11$
$1 \star 7 = 15$
$4 \star 3 = 10$
$6 \star 2 = ?$
Hint: Try doubling.

4 $6 \# 4 = 5$
$7 \# 1 = 4$
$3 \# 5 = 4$
$4 \# 2 = 3$
$3 \# 1 = ?$
Hint: Try adding.

5 $3 \heartsuit 2 = 1$
$5 \heartsuit 1 = 16$
$8 \heartsuit 2 = 36$
$7 \heartsuit 4 = 9$
$6 \heartsuit 1 = ?$
Hint: Try subtracting.

6 $7 \vee 2 = 18$
$1 \vee 5 = 12$
$3 \vee 2 = 10$
$6 \vee 4 = 20$
$2 \vee 4 = ?$
Hint: Try adding.

7 $8 \oslash 2 = 18$
$2 \oslash 8 = 12$
$3 \oslash 5 = 11$
$1 \oslash 3 = 5$
$4 \oslash 3 = ?$
Hint: Try doubling.

8 $8 \blacktriangle 3 = 7$
$4 \blacktriangle 2 = 4$
$6 \blacktriangle 6 = 9$
$2 \blacktriangle 7 = 8$
$10 \blacktriangle 2 = ?$
Hint: Try halving.

9 Now make up a challenge using a strange maths symbol of your own.

30

Matchstick puzzles

In each exercise, use matchsticks to build the shapes that are given above the tables. Now continue the pattern, following the rule you have observed. Complete the table and say what you see. Use the pattern to predict the number of matches you would need for the tenth figure.

1

Number of triangles	1	2	3	4	5	→	10
Number of matches						→	

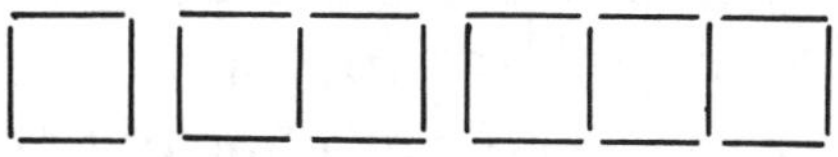

2

Number of squares	1	2	3	4	5	→	10
Number of matches						→	

3

Number of hexagons	1	2	3	4	5	→	10
Number of matches						→	

4

Number of houses	1	2	3	4	5	→	10
Number of matches						→	

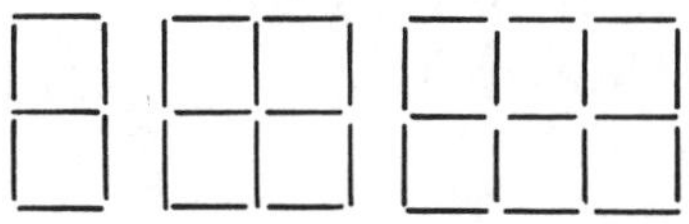

5

Number of double squares	1	2	3	4	5	→	10
Number of matches						→	

6 Make up a puzzle of your own.

EASY HUH?

Problem solving:
Your own strategy   1

PLAN

TO SOLVE
PROBLEMS

1. THINK ABOUT IT.

2. WRITE DOWN
THE ANSWER.

1   Nancy and Lucy each began reading *The Babysitters' Club* on Monday. Nancy reads 9 pages each day and Lucy reads 7 pages each day.

     On what day of the week will Nancy finish reading 54 pages? What page will Lucy be finishing on that day?

2   When Ritu returned to the library the book she had borrowed, she read the following notice about fines:

     If a book is 1 day overdue, the fine is 1p; for 2 days it is 2p, for 3 days, 4p, for 4 days, 8p, and so on.

     If Ritu has to pay a fine of 64p, how many days overdue is her book?

3   Salma and Becky took a holiday job strawberry picking. Salma filled 4 buckets of strawberries while Becky filled 3 buckets.

     How many buckets will Salma fill while Becky fills 24?

4   In a game of darts, a person can score 7 points if the dart lands in circle A, and 5 points if the dart lands in shaded area B.

     Jim threw 3 darts to area A and 3 darts to area B. If Michael threw only one dart to area A and beat Jim by 1 point, how many of his darts landed in area B?

5   Mr and Mrs Healthy have 3 children. The oldest child drinks 1 pint of milk in 2 days. The two younger children together drink 3 pints of milk in 2 days, while the parents drink 1 pint of milk in 3 days.

     How many pints of milk does the Healthy family drink in 6 days?

6   Heidi has some coins in her purse. She has twice as many 10p coins as 5p. She has one less 20p coin than she has 10p, and she has four 50p coins. The combined value of her 20p and 50p coins is £3.

     How many coins of each value does Heidi have?

Problem solving:
Your own strategy 2

1 Scott was given his pocket money on Sunday. On Monday he spent £2.50 on a present. On Tuesday he did some gardening and was paid £8. On Wednesday he bought a drink for 80p.

   If Scott now has £9.20, how much pocket money was he given?

2 When Leah and her two children, Andrew and Ramah, stepped onto a scale, it showed 127 kg as their total weight. When Andrew got off the scale showed 103 kg, and when Ramah got off and Andrew stepped back on the scale it showed 89 kg.

   How much did Leah and each of her two children weigh?

3 There are 35 people in a restaurant; 25 drink coffee and 14 drink lemonade. Everyone has either one or both of the drinks.

   How many people had both?

4 Shing started reading a new novel. She read 11 pages on the first night, 9 pages on the second night, 7 pages on the third night and so on, continuing this pattern.

   If the novel has 36 pages, how long will it take her to finish reading it?

5 Miranda bought some sweets and gave 4 of them to each of 3 friends. If she had 5 sweets left, how many did she buy?

6 Mrs Chong bought 5 ice-creams for £4 and 3 packets of chips for £3.60.

   How much did each ice-cream cost?

7 Miss Major had 120 five pound tickets for the end-of-year concert. She sold a quarter of the tickets on the first day.

   How many more tickets does Miss Major have to sell?

8 If 3 apples are worth 2 oranges, how many oranges are 12 apples worth?

9 I can buy 2 folders for £5. How many can I buy for £25?

10 I can buy 6 mugs for £18. How many mugs can I buy for (a) £9 and (b) £36?

Measurement puzzles

You could use containers and water to act out these problems, or you could draw diagrams in your book for each one, stating carefully what you are doing at every stage. For example, you could start problem 1(a) like this:

Fill the 7 litre bucket with water.

1 The two buckets shown here are marked 7 litres and 3 litres. They have no other markings.

Show how these two buckets can be used to measure exactly:
(a) 4 litres of water;
(b) 1 litre of water;
(c) 2 litres of water;
(d) 5 litres of water;
(e) 9 litres of water.

2 Make up a puzzle of your own.

Fraction fun

In these puzzles, some of the digits or fractions have been blotted out.

Find the missing numbers.

1 $\frac{1}{2} \times \square = 5$

2 $\square \times 8 = 4$

3 $\frac{1}{4} \times \square = 3$

4 $\frac{1}{4} \times \square = 6$

5 $\square \times 18 = 9$

6 $\square \times 24 = 12$

7 $\square \times 24 = 6$

8 $\square \times 12 = 3$

9 $\frac{1}{10} \times \square = 3$

10 $\square \times 40 = 4$

11 $\square \times 40 = 10$

12 $\square \times 40 = 20$

13 $\square \times 40 = 8$

14 $\frac{1}{5} \times \square = 8$

15 $\frac{1}{5} \times \square = 10$

16 $\square \times 22 = 11$

17 $\frac{1}{3} \times \square = 9$

18 $\frac{1}{4} \times \square = 4$

19 $\frac{1}{5} \times \square = 4$

20 $\frac{1}{10} \times \square = 9$

21 $\square \times 18 = 6$

22 $\square \times 60 = 30$

23 $\frac{1}{4} \times \square = 8$

24 $\square \times 15 = 3$

25 $\square \times 15 = 5$

26 $\square \times 25 = 5$

27 $\square \times 30 = 3$

28 $\square \times 30 = 5$

29 $\frac{1}{5} \times \square = 6$

30 $\frac{1}{8} \times \square = 3$

Coin puzzles

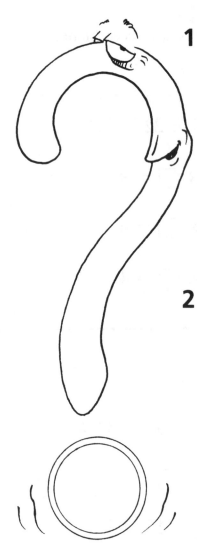

1 I have two piles of coins. Work out how many coins there are in each pile if:
(a) the first pile has 7 more than the second and there are 47 coins altogether;
(b) the first pile has 8 more than the second and there are 34 coins altogether;
(c) the first pile has 7 fewer than the second and there are 23 coins altogether;
(d) the first pile has 3 times as many as the second and there are 48 coins altogether;
(e) the first pile has 4 times as many as the second and there are 30 coins altogether.

2 I have three piles of coins. Calculate how many coins there are in each pile if:
(a) the second pile has 3 more than the first, the third has 3 more than the second and there are 27 coins altogether;
(b) the first pile has 9 more than the second, the third has 1 less than the second and there are 41 coins altogether;
(c) the second pile has twice as many as the first, the third has twice as many as the second and there are 56 coins altogether;
(d) the second pile has twice as many as the first, the third has half as many as the first and there are 21 coins altogether;
(e) the second pile has twice as many as the first, the third has twice as many as the second and the third has 9 more than the first;
(f) the first pile has 3 times as many as the third, the second has 3 more than the third and there are 38 coins altogether.

Problems on a dartboard

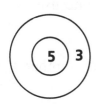

1 In one game of darts, 3 and 5 are the only possible scores in one throw.
   (a) What scores are possible?
   (b) What scores are impossible?

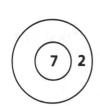

2 In another game of darts, 2 and 7 are the only possible values for a throw.
   (a) What scores are possible?
   (b) What scores are impossible?

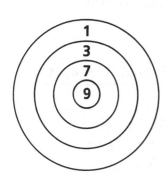

3 Robert threw four darts at this dartboard and all four hit a target.
   Which of the following numbers could his total score have been?

17, 22, 25, 18, 24, 11, 16, 31
What other totals could he have got?

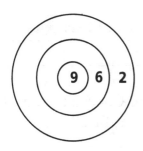

4 In a game of darts in which 9, 6 and 2 are the only possible scores, calculate:
   (a) the smallest number of throws needed to score exactly 34;
   (b) the greatest number of throws needed to score exactly 34.

Problem solving: Using tables 2

To answer these questions, you could draw up tables and use guess-and-check.

I DO ALL MY PROBLEM SOLVING USING A TABLE.

1 Michelle and her younger sister, Mia, bought their mother a bracelet for her birthday.

　　If Michelle decided to contribute twice as much as Mia and the bracelet cost £24, how much did each girl pay?

Michelle's contribution	Mia's contribution	Total cost

2 The sum of the ages of three children is 35. The oldest, Imran, is twice the age of the youngest, Bruce. Gordon is 3 years older than Bruce.

　　How old is Imran?

Imran	Gordon	Bruce	Sum of their ages

3 The sum of the ages of three sisters — Monique, Laura and Amy — is 25. Monique is the oldest. Amy is 7 years younger than Monique. Laura is 3 years older than Amy.

　　What are the ages of the three girls?

Monique	Laura	Amy	Sum of their ages

4 Lemon drops come in packages of 3 for 20p. Chocolate mints cost 5p each. Tom bought 20 sweets and spent £1.20.

　　How many of each kind did he buy?

Lemon drops (20p a pkt)	Chocolate mints (5p each)	Total spent

5 Raspberries cost £3 for 1 kg and grapes cost £4 for 1 kg.

　　How many kilograms of each did Mrs Morgan buy if:

(a) she spent £18 and had 5 kg of fruit?

(b) she spent £12? Is there only one answer to this?

Raspberries	Grapes	Cost

Solutions

What's the value? (page 6)

This is a very difficult challenge, especially since the way to discover the value of each shape cannot be found by taking the equations in order. Children have to work out where to start and how to proceed from the known to the unknown. However, they usually enjoy the puzzle and get a real sense of achievement when they complete it.

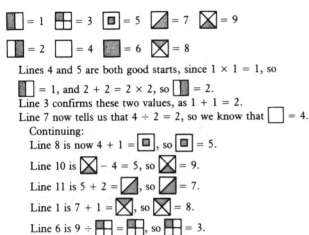

Lines 4 and 5 are both good starts, since $1 \times 1 = 1$, so

▯ = 1, and $2 + 2 = 2 \times 2$, so ▯ = 2.

Line 3 confirms these two values, as $1 + 1 = 2$.

Line 7 now tells us that $4 \div 2 = 2$, so we know that ▯ = 4.

Continuing:

Line 8 is now $4 + 1 = $ ▣, so ▣ = 5.

Line 10 is ⊠ $- 4 = 5$, so ⊠ = 9.

Line 11 is $5 + 2 = $ ◣, so ◣ = 7.

Line 1 is $7 + 1 = $ ⊠, so ⊠ = 8.

Line 6 is $9 \div$ ⊞ $= $ ⊞, so ⊞ = 3.

Line 2 is $2 \times 3 = $ ▨, so ▨ = 6.

The last few lines need not be done in this order.

Rolling boxes (page 7)

Children are not expected to visualise the position of the symbols as the boxes are rolled. They should carry out the experiments.

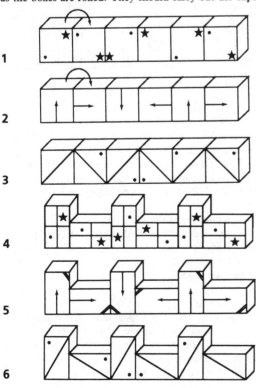

Find my rule (page 8)

	Rule	Missing numbers		Rule	Missing numbers
1	×4, +7	12, 19	6	×9, −5	45, 40
2	−7, ×6	3, 18	7	−4, ×7	2, 14
3	−3, ×9	6, 54	8	÷3, ×8	2, 16
4	÷2, + 5	3, 8	9	÷4, ×5	4, 20
5	×8, −11	48, 37	10	×6, ÷2	6; 48, 24

Making up their own rules allows children to be creative and may stretch them further. They may find that the operations and numbers need to be chosen with care if they wish to avoid using decimals or negative members.

Digits and numbers (page 9)

1	9995	6	9876	11	9990
2	1005	7	9872	12	10 000
3	1000	8	532	13	11 111
4	99 999	9	235	14	88 888
5	1023	10	1011	15	9870

Picture graphs (page 10)

1. (a) 18 (6 × 3)
   (b) 15 (5 × 3)
   (c) 12 (4 × 3)
   (d) chips; 21 (7 × 3)
   (e) pies; 3 (1 × 3)
   (f) 84 (28 × 3)
   (g) 6 sandwiches were sold;
       ∴ 9 were left.

2. Note that since ⬭ = 4 balls, ⬩ = 2 balls.
   (a) (i) 24 (6 × 4)
       (ii) 8 (2 × 4)
       (iii) 6 ($1\frac{1}{2}$ × 4)
       (iv) 18 ($4\frac{1}{2}$ × 4)
   (b) 72

3. This provides children with an opportunity to pose their own questions. This is a vital and often neglected part of the data handling process.

Problem solving: Working systematically 1 (page 11)

1.

2. Altogether there are 27 possible colour combinations. Given here are the remaining 25.
   Children should be encouraged to work them out systematically — without some guidance and discussion, it is doubtful whether they would find most of the possibilities.

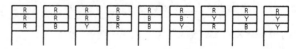

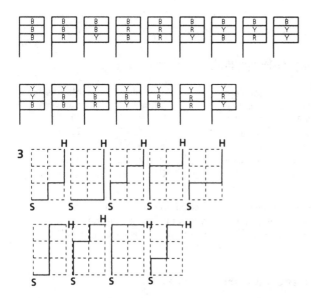

3

4 There are only two other possible patterns.

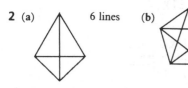

How many? (page 12)

In questions 1, 3 and 5, working systematically and counting all the different sized shapes is essential. Some children may decide to set out work in a table for clarity and organisation.

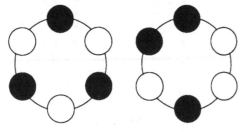

1 20 triangles: 12 single, 6 middle-sized, 2 large.

2 (a) 6 lines **(b)** 10 lines

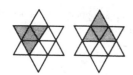

3 18 parallelograms: 6 small, 7 double (illustrated below), 2 treble, 2 quadruple, 1 large.

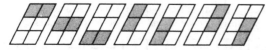

4 10 segments: XY, XZ, XU, XW, YZ, YU, YW, ZU, ZW, UW

5 18 squares: 8 single, 5 (2 × 2), 4 (3 × 3), 1 (4 × 4)

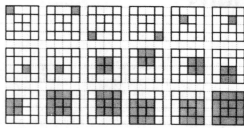

Multiplication table squares (page 13)

This is an exciting way to test and reinforce multiplication tables. Children can also make up other exercises and test each other.

1

X	3	5	4	7
2	6	10	8	14
8	24	40	32	56
3	9	15	12	21
9	27	45	36	63

2

X	4	6	2	7
5	20	30	10	35
3	12	18	6	21
8	32	48	16	56
6	24	36	12	42

The missing horizontal number is 2, since 5 × 2 = 10. The missing vertical numbers are 3 and 8, since 3 × 6 = 18 and 4 × 8 = 32.

3

X	2	3	9	5
2	4	6	18	10
8	16	24	72	40
7	14	21	63	35
4	8	12	36	20

4

X	7	4	11	5
2	14	8	22	10
3	21	12	33	15
9	63	36	99	45
4	28	16	44	20

5

X	3	8	5	10
4	12	32	20	40
5	15	40	25	50
3	9	24	15	30
9	27	72	45	90

6

X	9	2	7	8
3	27	6	21	24
8	72	16	56	64
6	54	12	42	48
2	18	4	14	16

7

X	5	4	6	8
1	5	4	6	8
6	30	24	36	48
9	45	36	54	72
4	20	16	24	32

8

X	5	2	10	8
5	25	10	50	40
8	40	16	80	64
3	15	6	30	24
10	50	30	100	80

How does it start? (page 14)

This can be made into a challenging game that children can have fun playing. One says: 'I think of a number, I add 3 to it, I multiply the result by 2 and my answer is 14. Find the number I first thought of'. The game can be played for hours, and children love it.

To find the number that belongs in the START circle of the example, begin with the end circle and work backwards, using the inverse of each given operation.

The inverse of add is subtract.
The inverse of subtract is add.
The inverse of multiply is divide.
The inverse of divide is multiply.

The reason for this is that if in the original flow chart the total of 14 was reached by multiplying a number by 2, to find that number by working backwards we must divide 14 by 2, so that the number must be 7. Similarly, if 7 was the result of adding 3 to a number, we find the number by subtracting 3 from 7.

1 ②← | Subtract 4: 6 − 4 = 2 | ← | Divide by 3: 18 ÷ 3 = 6 | ← ⑱

2 ⑦← | Add 5: 2 + 5 = 7 | ← | Divide by 3: 6 ÷ 3 = 2 | ← ⑥

3 ⑤← | Subtract 7: 12 − 7 = 5 | ← | Multiply by 2: 6 × 2 = 12 | ← ⑥

4 ⑤← | Subtract 3: 8 − 3 = 5 | ← | Divide by 3: 24 ÷ 3 = 8 | ← | Add 10: 14 + 10 = 24 | ← ⑭

5 ④← | Find the square root of 16 (i.e. 4) or ask 'what number squared is 16?' | ← | Add 6: 10 + 6 = 16 | ← | Multiply by 2: 5 × 2 = 10 | ← ⑤

6 Whilst investigating using different end numbers, children will encounter numbers other than positive whole numbers. A calculator may be useful here.

Investigating magic squares (page 15)

1 Yes; the sum is 21.
2 Yes; the sum is 45.

3 (**a**) The sum is 12. (**b**) The sum is 30.

16	2	12
6	10	14
8	18	4

(**c**) The sums are 45, 75 and 150 respectively.

(**d**) The sum is $7\frac{1}{2}$.

4	$\frac{1}{2}$	3
$\frac{3}{2}$	$\frac{5}{2}$	$\frac{7}{2}$
2	$\frac{9}{2}$	1

(**e**) The sums are $16\frac{1}{2}$ (for $+\frac{1}{2}$) and $13\frac{1}{2}$ (for $-\frac{1}{2}$). In each case the square is still magic.

4 Yes.

Counting cubes (page 16)

Most children will find it necessary to build the towers in order to count the cubes in each layer, and can use the cubes to check their answers. They should be encouraged to look for patterns.

1 (**a**)

top	1
2nd	3
Total	4

(**b**)

top	1
2nd	3
3rd	6
Total	10

2 (**a**)

top	2
2nd	6
Total	8

(**b**)

top	2
2nd	6
3rd	12
Total	20

(**c**)

top	1
2nd	3
3rd	6
4th	10
Total	20

(**c**)

top	2
2nd	6
3rd	12
4th	20
Total	40

3 (**a**)

top	4
Total	4

(**b**)

top	4
2nd	16
Total	20

(**c**)

top	4
2nd	16
3rd	36
Total	56

4 (**a**)

top	1
2nd	9
Total	10

(**b**)

top	1
2nd	9
3rd	25
Total	35

(**c**)

top	1
2nd	9
3rd	25
4th	49
Total	84

Puzzles with shapes (page 17)

1 triangle and   square

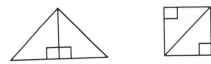

2 (**a**)

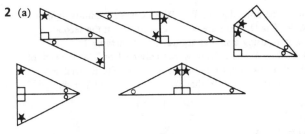

(**b**)

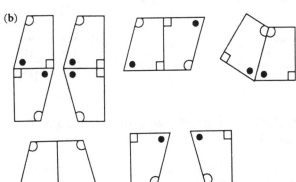

41

Letter values (page 18)

1 B = 5

$$\begin{array}{r} 51 \\ \times\ 5 \\ \hline 255 \end{array}$$

2 C = 6

$$\begin{array}{r} 61 \\ \times\ 6 \\ \hline 366 \end{array}$$

3 A = 6

$$\begin{array}{r} 46 \\ \times\ 6 \\ \hline 276 \end{array}$$

4 M = 2
N = 3

$$\begin{array}{r} 23 \\ \times\ 3 \\ \hline 69 \end{array}$$

5 U = 2
V = 4
W = 7

$$\begin{array}{r} 247 \\ \times\ 6 \\ \hline 1482 \end{array}$$

6 Since RR must equal 11 (as P + Q must be less than 22), the possible solutions are

$$\begin{array}{r} 9 \\ +\ 2 \\ \hline 11 \end{array} \quad \begin{array}{r} 8 \\ +\ 3 \\ \hline 11 \end{array} \quad \begin{array}{r} 7 \\ +\ 4 \\ \hline 11 \end{array}$$

$$\begin{array}{r} 6 \\ +\ 5 \\ \hline 11 \end{array} \quad \text{and} \quad \begin{array}{r} 2 \\ +\ 9 \\ \hline 11 \end{array}$$

7 Since the units digit of D + E + F is F, the units digit of D + E is 0, so D + E = 10. Therefore, D = 1 and E = 9. F is any other one-digit number: 2, 3, 4, 5, 6, 7, 8 or 0.

8 J = 8
K = 9

$$\begin{array}{r} 89 \\ +\ 9 \\ \hline 98 \end{array}$$

9 G = 1
H = 0
L = 9

$$\begin{array}{r} 91 \\ +\ 9 \\ \hline 100 \end{array}$$

10 C must be an even number and C + C + C + C is less than 10, therefore C = 2.
    D = 3, as D + D + D + D ends in 2, and E = 9

$$\begin{array}{r} 23 \\ 23 \\ 23 \\ +\ 23 \\ \hline 92 \end{array}$$

11 Since the units digit of Y + W + X is Y, the units digit of W + X is O, therefore W + X = 10. From the second column, using a similar argument and carrying 1, 1 + W + Y = 10. Now W can only be 1 or 2, as the sum of the three two-digit numbers is less than 300. By trial and error it is then shown that W = 1, X = 9 and Y = 8.

12 S = 1
P = 3
Q = 4

$$\begin{array}{r} 34 \\ 34 \\ +\ 43 \\ \hline 111 \end{array}$$

13 W = 1
T = 0
V = 9

$$\begin{array}{r} 101 \\ -\ 91 \\ \hline 10 \end{array}$$

14 Only 3 × 5 ends in a 5; therefore N = 5, L = 1 and M = 8.

$$\begin{array}{r} 185 \\ 185 \\ +\ 185 \\ \hline 555 \end{array}$$

15 B = 1
A = 9
D = 0

$$\begin{array}{r} 991 \\ +\ 119 \\ \hline 1110 \end{array}$$

Problem solving: Working systematically 2 (page 19)

It is important in all these problems for children to find their own ways of recording.

1 (a) 3 presents (b) 12 presents

2 20 presents

3 (a) 6 code words:
A B C
A C B
B A C
B C A
C A B
C B A

(b) 27: First start with A (illustrated), then with B and then with C.
A A A
A A B
A A C
A B A
A B B
A B C
A C A
A C B
A C C

4

1st	2nd	3rd
A	M	S
A	S	M
M	A	S
M	S	A
S	A	M
S	M	A

5 4 ways:

Bowl	Fish			
A	4	3	2	1
B	1	2	3	4

6

Shirts	Shorts	Jumpers
blue	navy	black
blue	white	black
blue	navy	red
blue	white	red
yellow	navy	black
yellow	white	black
yellow	navy	red
yellow	white	red

7 2 g
5 g
7 g
10 g
12 g
15 g
17 g

8 Giving the amounts all in pence 10, 20, 30, 40, 50, 60, 70, 80, 90, 100

Problem solving: Working backwards (page 20)

To find all the solutions, we started with the final number and then worked backwards.

1 6: 9 multiplied by 2 gives 18, or 18 divided by 2 will give 9. Then 6 has to be added to 3 to give 9 or 3 must be subtracted from 9 to give 6. Now work through the problem to check the answer: 6 + 3 = 9; 9 × 2 = 18.

2 5: 10 is doubled to give 20 and 5 is doubled to give 10.

3 12: 6 is added to 4 to give 10, and 12 is halved to give 6.

4 13: 6 is doubled to give 12, and 7 is subtracted from 13 to give 6.

5 10: 5 added to 9 gives 14, and 10 halved gives 5.

6 8: 4 doubled gives 8, and 8 halved gives 4.

7 6: Halving and then doubling or doubling and then halving will result in any number that you start with.

8 5 **9** 8 **10** 9 **11** 4 **12** 16 **13** 4 **14** 3 **15** 8
16 9 **17** 3 **18** 4

19 2: Before the result was halved, it was 6; before 2 was added it was 4, and before it was squared it was 2.

Problem solving: Using tables 1 (page 21)

1 Students can use guess-and-check, drawing up the table:

Esi	Marc	Total marbles
12	9	21

Alternatively, they can act out the problem. Start with 21 marbles or counters and give three to Esi, since she has three more than Marc.

Now the remaining 18 marbles can be divided equally between them; therefore Esi has 12 marbles (3 + 9) and Marc has 9 marbles.

2

Ice-creams (£1)	Ice-lollies (50p)	Total spent
6	8	£10

3

	5p coins	10p coins	Total coins	Total amount
(a)	4	2	6	40p
(b)	6	5	11	80p
(c)	3	3	6	45p
(d)	2	6	8	70p
(e)	6	2	8	50p

Problem solving: With extra information (page 22)

Children should discuss which information they did not use.

They could be asked to make up some problems that give unnecessary information, or even to create some that have insufficient information.

	Solutions	Extra information
1	Steve weighed 32 kg.	• Yoko weighed 9 kg more than Steve.
2	Kate Zara Lisa Layla 95 cm 90 cm 92 cm 98 cm	• Zara and Lisa are cousins. • Layla is 13 years old.
3	Kate Lisa Layla Zara 252 cm 255 cm 260 cm 265 cm	• Zara jumped 4 cm further than her best friend, Rhonda.
4	(diagram of people around a circle: Marc, Grandma Happy, Mrs Happy, Mr Happy, Jenny)	• Last night Jenny sat next to her brother and they had a fight. • Marc did not like the vegetable soup and his mother made him eat it. • Jenny loved the cake Grandma made.

Perimeter and area investigation (page 23)

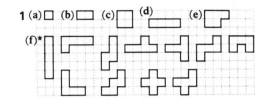

1 (a) (b) (c) (d) (e) (f)*

* The figures in (f) are eleven of the twelve pentominoes. Figure (e) is the twelfth.

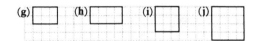

(g) (h) (i) (j)

2 It is not possible.

Growing squares and triangles (page 24)

1 (a)

Side (cm)	Perimeter (cm)	Area (sq. cm)
1	4	1
2	8	4
3	12	9
4	16	16
5	20	25
6	24	36
10	40	100
	The perimeter of each square is four times the length of a side.	The area of each square is the square of the length of a side.

(b) The perimeter and the area can in each case be predicted by following the patterns given in (a).

2 (a)

Side (units)	Perimeter (units)	Area (triang-grids)
1	3	1
2	6	4
3	9	9
4	12	16
5	15	25
6	18	36
10	30	100
	The perimeter of each equilateral triangle is three times the length of a side.	The area of each equilateral triangle (*measured in triangular grids*) is the square of the length of a side.

(b) The perimeters and areas can be predicted by following the patterns given in (a).

Perimeter puzzles (page 25)

Squared paper is essential for these exercises.

Children should check their figures to make sure they are all different — that no one figure is the same as another, but turned to a different position.

1 (a) 16 cm

(b)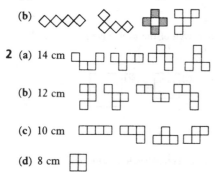

2 (a) 14 cm

(b) 12 cm

(c) 10 cm

(d) 8 cm

3 Since all four sides of a square are equal, each side is 9 cm. Numbers 4 and 5 can also be done using guess-and-check and drawing up a table.

4 From the diagram, the perimeter (60 m) has six equal sections; therefore one section is 10 m and the length is 20 m (2 × 10). If children have difficulty with this problem, solve a simpler one using a perimeter of 6 m and drawing the figure on squared paper.

5 This perimeter (48 m) has eight equal sections; therefore the width (one section) is 6 m and the length (three sections) is 18 m. Similarly, a simpler problem can be solved using a perimeter of 8 m and drawing the figure on squared paper:

1 cm ☐☐☐ 1 cm
3 cm (top) 3 cm (bottom)

Next use a perimeter of 16 m:

6 cm
2 cm

6 The large table has 10 equal sections to total 20 m. Therefore the side of a square is 2 m and the perimeter of a square is 8 m.

Palindromic numbers (page 26)

1 (a)
```
    59
    95
   ---
   154
   451
   ---
   605
   506
  ----
  1111
```

(b)
```
    78
    87
   ---
   165
   561
   ---
   726
   627
  ----
  1353
  3531
  ----
  4884
```

(c)
```
    79
    97
   ---
   176
   671
   ---
   847
   748
  ----
  1595
  5951
  ----
  7546
  6457
 -----
 14003
 30041
 -----
 44044
```

2 (a) 11, 22, 33, 44, 55, 66, 77, 88, 99 are palindromic numbers.

(b) One-stage palindromic numbers: 12, 13, 14, 15, 16, 17, 18, 20, 21, 23, 24, 25, 26, 27, 29, 30, 31, 32, 34, 35, 36, 38, 40, 41, 42, 43, 45, 47, 50, 51, 52, 53, 54, 56, 60, 61, 62, 63, 65, 70, 71, 72, 74, 80, 81, 83, 90, 92

(c) Two-stage numbers: 19, 28, 37, 39, 46, 48, 49, 57, 58, 64, 67, 73, 75, 76, 82, 84, 85, 91, 93, 94

(d) Three-stage numbers: 59, 68, 86, 95

(e) Four-stage numbers: 69, 78, 87, 96

(f) Six-stage numbers: 79, 97

To carry out the above investigation is not as big a task as it may seem, for when children find that a number such as 18 is a one-stage palindromic number, it is immediately evident that so also is 81. However many stages a number takes to become palindromic, the number formed by reversing its digits will take the same number of stages.

The numbers 89 and 98, however, are not palindromic even after 20 stages, and children should be warned about this. They can be given calculators to attempt these challenges, although finding which numbers less than 100 are palindromic is an excellent way to practise addition of two-, three- and four-digit numbers. Children will be much more motivated to do these additions than just to work out a lot of sums without an overall purpose.

Shopping at a barter market (page 27)

Children can draw up a table in order to answer the questions.

1 (a) 6 tomatoes
(b) 15 apples
(c) 30 potatoes

2 (a) 5 lettuces
(b) 4 lettuces
(c) 6 lettuces

3 (a) 10 apples
(b) 50 apples
(c) 25 apples
(d) 30 apples

4 (a) 5 lettuces
(b) 10 tomatoes
(c) 50 potatoes

Lettuces	Tomatoes	Apples	Potatoes
1	2	5	10
2	4	10 (3a)	20
3	6 (1a)	15 (1b)	30 (1c)
4 (2b)	8	20	40
5 (2a)	10	25	50
6 (2c)	12	30	60
7	14	35	70
8	16	40	80

5 10 tomatoes = 5 lettuces
10 apples = 2 lettuces
∴ Total trade = 7 lettuces

6 (a) 8 lettuces
(b) 40 apples
(c) 80 potatoes

Using a table is one way to solve these problems. Another method uses ratios or proportion.

For 2(a): since 2 tomatoes are worth 1 lettuce, 10 tomatoes (which is 5 lots of 2) are worth 5 lettuces (5 lots of 1).

For 2(b): since 5 apples are worth 1 lettuce, 20 apples (which is 4 lots of 5) are worth 4 lettuces (which is 4 lots of 1).

Tree diagrams (page 28)

1

H H H	Note the
H H T	systematic way in
H T H	which the
H T T	possibilities are
T H H	written out.
T H T	
T T H	
T T T	

2

Bread	Filling
brown	honey
brown	cheese
brown	Marmite
brown	tuna
brown	salad
white	honey
white	cheese
white	Marmite
white	tuna
white	salad

3 Reading along all the branches, there are nine possibilities:

train/walking	coach/walking	car/walking
train/bus	coach/bus	car/bus
train/taxi	coach/taxi	car/taxi

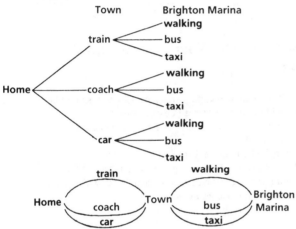

Number squares (page 29)

In solving these problems, you can use guess-and-check and/or the given procedure and starting points.

1

2	2	1	5	10	A = 2
5	3	5	4	17	B = 5
3	3	1	4	11	C = 1
5	4	2	1	12	D = 4
15	12	9	14		E = 3

From the first row,
C + B = 6. Now, either
use guess-and-check for B and
C or use the fact that
C + B = 6 to find the value of
D in the fourth row or the
fourth column. For the latter
method:

B + D + A + C = 12
6 + D + 2 = 12,
since A = 2 and B + C = 6
∴ D = 4

Since B + C = 6, we can
work out C in the third
column:

$\underline{C + B} + C + A = 9$
$\quad 6 \quad + C + 2 = 9$
∴ C = 1

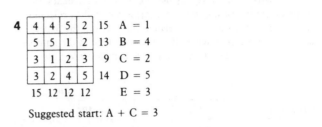

2

2	1	2	3	8	A = 1
4	4	1	3	12	B = 3
5	2	4	1	12	C = 4
1	5	3	4	13	D = 2
12	12	10	11		E = 5

Suggested start: A + B = 4

3

3	5	1	2	11	A = 2
3	1	4	2	10	B = 4
5	2	1	3	11	C = 1
1	2	4	5	12	D = 5
12	10	10	12		E = 3

Suggested start: C + D = 6

4

4	4	5	2	15	A = 1
5	5	1	2	13	B = 4
3	1	2	3	9	C = 2
3	2	4	5	14	D = 5
15	12	12	12		E = 3

Suggested start: A + C = 3

Strange maths symbols (page 30)

Children are not expected to use symbols in writing the rules.

1 $\square \odot \triangle = \square + \triangle + 5$
$7 \odot 3 = 7 + 3 + 5$
$\qquad = 15$
Rule: Add the two numbers, then add 5.

2 $\square \wedge \triangle = \square - \triangle + 2$
$8 \wedge 2 = 8 - 2 + 2$
$\qquad = 8$
Rule: Subtract the second number from the first and add 2.

3 $\square \star \triangle = \square + 2 \times \triangle$
$6 \star 2 = 6 + 2 \times 2$
$\qquad = 10$
Rule: Double the second number and add the first to the result.

4 $\square \# \triangle = \dfrac{\square + \triangle}{2}$
$3 \# 1 = \dfrac{3 + 1}{2} = 2$
Rule: Add the two numbers and halve the result.

5 $\square \heartsuit \triangle = (\square - \triangle)^2$
$6 \heartsuit 1 = 5^2$
$\qquad = 25$
Rule: Subtract the second number from the first and square the result.

6 $\square \vee \triangle = (\square + \triangle) \times 2$
$2 \vee 4 = 12$
Rule: Add the two numbers and double the result.

7 $\square \oslash \triangle = 2 \times \square + \triangle$
$4 \oslash 3 = 8 + 3$
$\qquad = 11$
Rule: Double the first number and add the second to the result.

8 $\square \blacktriangle \triangle = \square \div 2 + \triangle$
$10 \blacktriangle 2 = 7$
Rule: Halve the first number and add the second to the result.

9 Making up their own symbols gives children a chance to explore further.

Matchstick puzzles (page 31)

Children will need to know their two, three and five times tables to succeed with these exercises. Encourage them to express each rule in words; in the rule formulas, □ stands for the number of original shapes.

1 The number of matches is twice the number of triangles plus 1. Many children will say that the number of matches is going up (or increasing) by 2, but this is not really a rule and they should be led to see the relationship between the figures and the number of matches. If they cannot predict the number for the tenth diagram, they will have to complete the table with figures 6 to 10.

Rule

Triangles	1	2	3	4	5	⟶ 10
Matches	3	5	7	9	11	⟶ 21

$2 \times \square + 1$

2

Squares	1	2	3	4	5	⟶ 10
Matches	4	7	10	13	16	⟶ 31

$3 \times \square + 1$

3

Hexagons	1	2	3	4	5	⟶ 10
Matches	6	11	16	21	26	⟶ 51

$5 \times \square + 1$

4

Houses	1	2	3	4	5	⟶ 10
Matches	6	11	16	21	26	⟶ 51

$5 \times \square + 1$

5

Double squares	1	2	3	4	5	⟶ 10
Matches	7	12	17	22	27	⟶ 52

$5 \times \square + 2$

Problem solving: Your own strategy 1 (page 32)

Children could draw up tables for questions 1, 2 and 3.

1

Day	Number of pages read	
	by Nancy	by Lucy
Monday	9	7
Tuesday	18	14
Wednesday	27	21
Thursday	36	28
Friday	45	35
Saturday	54	42

Therefore Nancy will finish page 54 on Saturday, and on that day Lucy will finish page 42.

2

Day	1	2	3	4	5	6	7
Fine	1p	2p	4p	8p	16p	32p	64p

Therefore Ritu's book is 7 days overdue.

3

Salma	4	8	12	16	20	24	28	32
Becky	3	6	9	12	15	18	21	24

Therefore Salma will fill 32 buckets in this time.

4 Use logical reasoning in this question.
Jim's score $= 3 \times 7 + 3 \times 5$
$= 36$
Michael's score $= 37$
Michael threw one dart in area A for 7 points, so his score in area B is 30. Therefore Michael threw 6 darts in area B.

5 In 6 days:
the eldest child drinks 3 pints;
the two younger children drink 9 pints
the parents drink 2 pints;
Altogether, the family drinks 14 pints of milk in 6 days.

6 Working backwards is a good strategy. Four 50p coins are worth £2, so her 20p coins are worth £1. Therefore Heidi has five 20p coins.
Since she has one less 20p coin than 10p, she has six 10p coins.
Since she has twice as many 10p coins as 5p, she has three 5p coins.

Her coins are therefore:

5p	10p	20p	50p
3	6	5	4

Problem solving: Your own strategy 2 (page 33)

These solutions show possible strategies. Children should be encouraged to find their own and explain them.

1 Start with the amount Scott has now and work backwards:
Scott has £9.20.
Before he bought the drink, he had £10.00.
Before he was paid for the gardening, he had £2.00.
Before he bought the present he had £4.50, which is the amount of his pocket money.

2 Again work backwards:
We know that Leah weighs 65 kg.
Without Ramah, the scale dropped 38 kg.
Without Andrew, the scale dropped 24 kg.
Therefore Ramah weighs 38 kg and Andrew weighs 24 kg.

3 Note that a total of 39 drinks are served to only 35 people. Therefore, 4 people drink both.

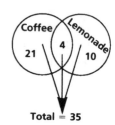

Total = 35

4 Draw up a table and look for a pattern.

Night	Pages read	Page reached
1	11	11
2	9	20
3	7	27
4	5	32
5	3	35
6	1	36

On the sixth night, Shing finished her novel.

5 Working backwards: 5 sweets left plus 12 sweets given away make a total of 17 sweets.

6 Each ice-cream cost 80p. The cost of the chips is unnecessary data.

7 Miss Major sold 30 tickets and has to sell 90 more. The cost of the ticket is unnecessary data.

8 3 apples = 2 oranges or, in a table:

6 apples = 4 oranges

12 apples = 8 oranges

Apples	Oranges
3	2
6	4
9	6
12	8

9 If 2 folders cost £5, I can buy:
   4 for £10
   6 for £15
   8 for £20
   10 for £25

10 6 mugs cost £18.
   (a) Halve both the amount of money and the number of mugs:
      3 mugs cost £9.
   (b) Double both the amount of money and the number of mugs:
      12 mugs cost £36.

Measurement puzzles (page 34)

1 (a) Fill the 7 ℓ bucket. From it, fill the smaller bucket, which will take 3 ℓ. 4 ℓ will remain.

(b) Continuing from (a), empty the 3 ℓ bucket.
   There are 4 ℓ left in the larger bucket; use this to refill the 3 ℓ bucket; 1 ℓ will remain.

(c) Fill the 3 ℓ bucket and pour the contents into the larger one.
   Repeat this. The larger bucket now contains 6 ℓ. Fill the 3 ℓ bucket again and from it fill the larger one, which will take 1 ℓ.
   2 ℓ will remain.

(d) Continuing from (c), first empty the larger bucket, then pour into it the water remaining in the small one (2 ℓ). Refill the 3 ℓ bucket and pour its contents into the larger one, which will then contain 5 ℓ.

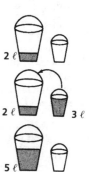

(e) The last stage of (c) has 7 ℓ in one bucket and 2 ℓ in the other, making a total of 9 ℓ.

Children may find other valid solutions.

Fraction fun (page 35)

Children should have counters — or some other concrete material — available if they want to work out the problems with the use of some tangible aid.

Children could ask:

1 10	Half of what number is 5?		**6** $\frac{1}{2}$	
2 $\frac{1}{2}$	What fraction of 8 is 4?		**7** $\frac{1}{4}$	
3 12	One quarter of what number is 3?		**8** $\frac{1}{4}$	
4 24	One quarter of what number is 6?		**9** 30	
5 $\frac{1}{2}$	What fraction of 18 is 9?		**10** $\frac{1}{10}$	

11 $\frac{1}{4}$	**16** $\frac{1}{2}$	**21** $\frac{1}{3}$	**26** $\frac{1}{5}$
12 $\frac{1}{2}$	**17** 27	**22** $\frac{1}{2}$	**27** $\frac{1}{10}$
13 $\frac{1}{5}$	**18** 16	**23** 32	**28** $\frac{1}{8}$
14 40	**19** 20	**24** $\frac{1}{4}$	**29** 30
15 50	**20** 90	**25** $\frac{1}{3}$	**30** 24

Fractions can be used to stimulate able children even though they are becoming less important in primary schools.

Coin puzzles (page 36)

Children can answer these questions either by using guess-and-check or by acting out the problems, as illustrated in 1(a) and (b) and in 2(a).

1 (a) Take 47 counters. Use 7 to begin the first pile. Now divide the remaining 40 equally between the two piles.
   (b) Take 34 counters. Use 8 to begin the first pile. Now divide the remaining 26 equally between the two piles.

	1st pile	2nd pile
(a)	27	20
(b)	21	13
(c)	8	15
(d)	36	12
(e)	24	6

2 (a) Take 27 counters. Use 3 to begin the second pile. Now, since the third pile has 3 more than the second, in fact it has 6 more than the first, so place 6 counters in the third pile. Now 18 counters remain, which are divided equally between the three.

	1st pile	2nd pile	3rd pile
(a)	6	9	12
(b)	20	11	10
(c)	8	16	32
(d)	6	12	3
(e)	3	6	12
(f)	21	10	7

Problems on a dartboard (page 37)

1 (a) 3, 5, 6, 8, 9, 10, 11, 12 and all further numbers are possible.
   (b) 1, 2, 4 and 7 are the only impossible scores. Most children will use trial and error. Once three consecutive possible scores are found — 8, 9 and 10 — there is no need to search further; you can add 3 to any of these, so that all remaining numbers are possible.

$3 + 3 = 6$
$3 + 5 = 8$
$3 + 3 + 3 = 9$
$5 + 5 = 10$
$3 + 3 + 5 = 11$
$3 + 3 + 3 + 3 = 12$
$3 + 5 + 5 = 13$
$3 + 3 + 3 + 5 = 14$
$5 + 5 + 5 = 15$

2 (a) 2, 4, 6, 7, 8, 9 and all further numbers are possible.
   (b) 1, 3 and 5 are the only impossible scores. This time, once we have two consecutive possible scores the search is over.

$2 + 2 = 4$
$2 + 2 + 2 = 6$
$7 = 7$
$2 + 2 + 2 + 2 = 8$
$2 + 7 = 9$

3 Since the scores are all odd numbers and since four odd numbers give an even number, none of the odd numbers is a possible total.

$9 + 7 + 3 + 3 = 22$
$9 + 9 + 3 + 1 = 22$
$7 + 7 + 3 + 1 = 18$
$9 + 9 + 3 + 3 = 24$
$7 + 3 + 3 + 3 = 16$

4 List all possible combinations that would achieve a score of 34.
   (a) Smallest number of throws is 6.
   (b) Greatest number of throws is 17.

9	6	2	No. of throws
0	0	17	17
0	1	14	15
0	2	11	13
0	3	8	11
2	0	8	10
0	4	5	9
2	2	2	6

Problem solving: Using tables 2 (page 38)

1

Michelle's contribution	Mia's contribution	Total cost
£16	£8	£24

2

Imran	Gordon	Bruce	Sum of their ages
16	11	8	35

It will be easier if you first guess Bruce's age and then work out the ages of the others.

3

Monique	Laura	Amy	Sum of their ages
12	8	5	25

4

Lemon drops (20p a pkt)	Chocolate mints (5p each)	Total spent
4 packages (12 sweets)	8	£1.20

5

	Raspberries at £3	Grapes at £4	Cost
(a)	2 kg	3 kg	£18
(b)	4 kg	0	£12
	0	3 kg	£12
	2 kg	1½ kg	
	3 kg	¾ kg	
	1 kg	2¼ kg	£12
	1⅓ kg	2 kg	
	2⅔ kg	1 kg	

There are many possible answers to 5(b) and only some are given here *in the table*. Children are unlikely to give more than the first two.

All the solutions can be represented on the graph; some are indicated by the dots:

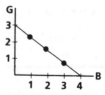

An informal discussion about all the possible solutions is worthwhile.